Jane Austen's

Pride
and Prejudice

A Colouring Journal

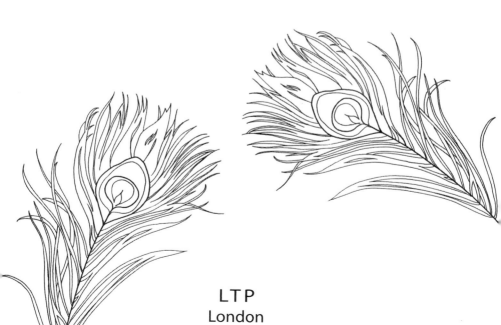

LTP
London

It is a truth universally acknowledged, that a single man in possession of a good fortune, must be in want of a wife.

'A woman must have a thorough knowledge of music, singing, drawing and dancing…'
Mr Darcy

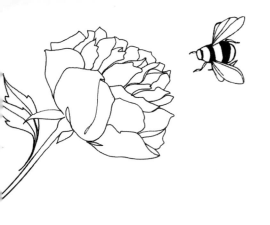

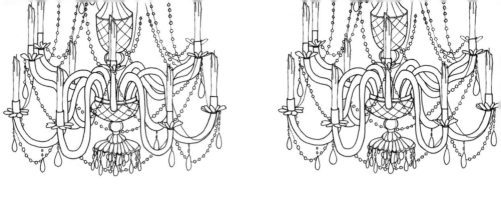

*To be fond of dancing was a certain
step towards falling in love.*

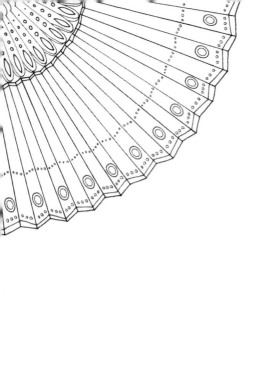

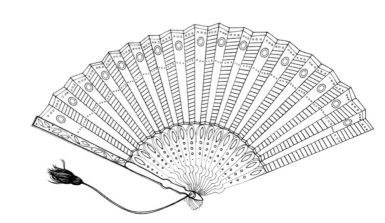

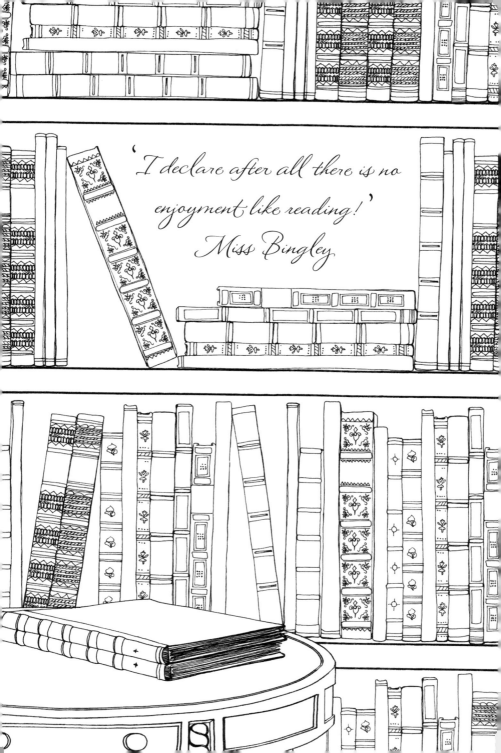

'*I declare after all there is no enjoyment like reading!*'
Miss Bingley

His sisters were fine women, with an air of decided fashion.

'She is tolerable; but not handsome enough to tempt *me*.'
Mr Darcy

'*I could easily forgive **his** pride,
if he had not mortified **mine**.*'

Elizabeth

'Oh! My sweetest Lizzy!
how rich and how great
you will be!'
Mrs Bennet

Darcy had never been
so bewitched by any
woman as he
was by her.

'A lady's imagination is very rapid;
it jumps from admiration to love, from love
to matrimony in a moment.'
Mr Darcy

They could talk of nothing but officers.

Hope was over, entirely over.

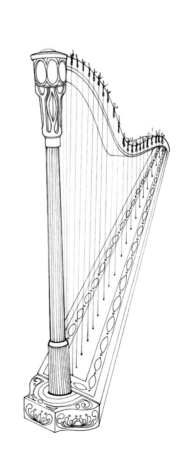

'Till this moment,
I never knew myself.'
Elizabeth

'You must allow me
to tell you how ardently
I admire and love you.'

Mr Darcy

'It is impossible that
he should still love me.'
Elizabeth

'How much
sooner one tires
of any thing than
of a book!'
Miss Bingley

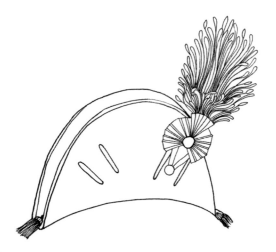

Angry people are not always wise.

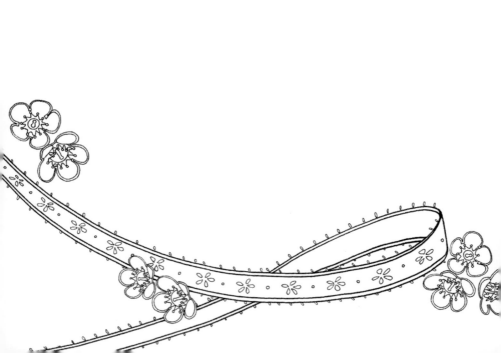

'*My good opinion, once lost, is lost forever.*'
Mr Darcy

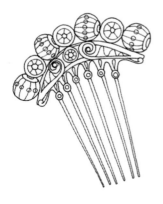

Her heart did whisper
that he had done it for her.

'*My* affections and wishes
are unchanged, but one word
from you will silence me
on this subject for ever.'
Mr Darcy

'I am the happiest creature in the world. Perhaps other people have said so before, but not one with such justice.'
Elizabeth

Never had she so honestly felt that
she could have loved him, as now...

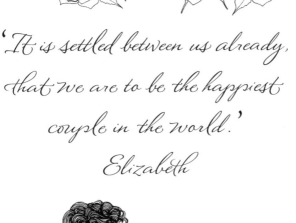

'It is settled between us already,
that we are to be the happiest
couple in the world.'
Elizabeth

LTP

1 The Coda Centre, 189 Munster Road,
London SW6 6AW
www.littletiger.co.uk

First published in Great Britain 2017
Copyright © Little Tiger Press 2017
Illustrations copyright © Chellie Carroll 2016
Chellie Carroll has asserted her right to be identified
as the illustrator of this work under the Copyright,
Designs and Patents Act, 1988

All rights reserved • ISBN 978-1-84869-562-7
Printed in China • LTP/2700/1672/1116
10 9 8 7 6 5 4 3 2 1